An introduction to

KINESIOLOGY

An Introduction to

KINESIOLOGY

b y

Brian H. Butler. B.A.

THE NATURAL WAY
TO
"BALANCED HEALTH"
& WELL - BEING

Find Solutions To:
Anxieties, Lack of Confidence, Mood
Swings, Emotional Stress, Fears and
Phobias, Dyslexia, Learning Problems,
Poor Memory, Low Energy

Allergies, Food Sensitivities and Dietary
Deficiencies, Supplement Selection

Backache, Stiff Shoulders, General
aches and pains, and most of the other
minor conditions that plague us all....

through Kinesiology!

A T.A.S.K. PUBLICATION ©1995

Dedication to Miss Stephanie P. L. Mills

Without whose constant, loyal support, and warm encouragement over the last now nearly thirty-five years, and her insistence that it was needed, this book, thought of for so long, would never have been written, and she who encouraged me to print 10,000 copies of the first edition. Her faith was justified!

Dedication to Siobhan Guthrie

After Siobhan trained in 1995, she went on to teach many classes. We set up T.A.S.K. Ireland over fifteen years ago. Her constant faithfulness to pure Applied Kinesiology; her outstanding dedication working on more effective ways to give our world the wonderful Kinesiological principles; are an inspiration to the students, graduates, and to all she meets.   B.H.B.

© 1990 by Brian H. Butler, B.A. D. O., F.A.S.K.
First Edition:10,000 Copies. June 1990
Second Edition:15,000 Copies. March 1995
Third Edition by T.A.S.K. Ireland in

January 2017 © Brian Butler

British Library Cataloguing in Publication Data
Butler, Brian Henry
Introduction to Kinesiology: Natural Way
to 'Balanced Health' and Well-Being.
New FOURTH edition for U.K. 2019
1. Title
612.76

ISBN 978 0 9943391 9 5

Published by T.A.S.K. BOOKS

Published with the assistance of https://angelkey.com.au
Printed in Great Britain in U.K., U.S.A. Australia & Ireland
2019 by Ingram Spark, Lightning Source

ACKNOWLEDGMENTS

Kinesiology is now the most powerful tool available to us in natural health care and in the promotion of well-being. I was indeed very fortunate to come across it in 1976, and be the one to pioneer the concept and practice in Britain and Europe. I want to express my deep gratitude to:

Dr. George Goodheart, D.C., for making the original discoveries which led to the development of Kinesiology.

Dr. John F. Thie, D.C. who against opposition made the basic concepts of Kinesiology available to the public.

Dr. John Blossom, D.C. who first introduced me to Kinesiology, helped relieve my daughter's pain and encouraged me to learn Kinesiology.

Gordon Stokes, my friend and mentor who inspired me, taught me brilliant teaching concepts & cemented my early training in Kinesiology, and who has always remained an enthusiastic supporter of my work through thick and thin.

Dr. Sheldon Deal, D.C. who has shared his knowledge so generously for so many years, and for the warm and dependable friendship of he and his wife Cindy.

Stephanie P. L. Mills, Lic.Ac, M.T.A.S. who came as a student, and stayed as a colleague and loyal supporter. Without her help, encouragement, regular balancing, the many acupunture treatments, her support at all the classes and courses we hold, her holding my head when all the difficulties, the pain and the discouragements threatened to overwhelm me and cause me to give up the struggle to continue to spread Kinesiology in the face of ridicule, and rejection, this book would not have been written.

Claire E. Moffat who takes care of the day to day office administration, and works part-time so diligently to keep up with all the business tasks, the letters, the calls, the appointments and take care of a family- always with a smile.

Balanced Health Instructors who are enthusiastically making basic Kinesiolgy available to people all over the country, in shows, talks, in weekend and evening classes.

To all these people I owe my continued success in spreading Kinesiology. To those I have not mentioned, students, trustees, and others who have helped me along the way, also goes my heartfelt appreciation.   Brian H. Butler. B.A.

WHAT IS IN THIS BOOK

Acknowledgments   iv
Preface Prediction v
What can Kinesiology help with? 1
Poor Health is pandemic. 2
How is Kinesiology done?. 3
How are imbalances corrected? 4
How does it help overcome problems? . 6
What if imbalances are not corrected? . . 7
Kinesiology helps prevention 8
The Environment we live in 11
Our food and water 12
Exercise 13
Our mental diet 14
Kinesiology a wholistic approach 15
The mental/emotional realm 15
Dietary and nutritional factors 17
Drugs and chemicals 18
Structural integrity 19
Energy and life force 21
Kinesiological Muscle Testing . . 23
Muscle Testing DON'Ts 23
Basic Muscle Testing procedure 24

Testing the Pectoralis Major Clavicular . 26
Testing the Supraspinatus muscle 28
Testing the Latissimus Dorsii muscle . . . 29
What if the muscle isn't strong. 30
Neuro-Vascular strengthening points . . 30
Neuro-Lymphatic strengthening points . . 31
What if the muscles won't strengthen? . . . 32

Emotional Stress Release **33**
Emotional stress release helps overwhelm 34
How E.S.R. was discovered 35
New solutions to old problems 38
A - Z Benefits of using E.S.R. 39
How to use the E.S.R. technique 41
Privacy and confidentiality is vital 42
Focussing hard on the problem 43
What is the result of using E.S.R. 44
Muscle testing is a language 45
Using muscle testing with E.S.R. 45
Procedure for muscle testing with E.S.R. 46
Frontal occipital holding and E.S.R. . . . 49
The origins of Kinesiology **51**
In conclusion 56

PREFACE PREDICTION

Applied Kinesiology was first discovered as a phenomenon in 1964. Although its components are ancient in origin, it is an entirely new concept.

New concepts take at least a generation to mature to the point where they cease being the inventors' and discoverers' off-spring, and become public property for all to enjoy the benefits.

New concepts are usually ridiculed, put down, refuted or ignored by other "*learned*" men. Those who dare to propagate new ideas find themselves the butt of jokes, and the target of attempts to discredit their integrity. This is a fact of history in practically every field of professional endeavour.

Nevertheless, Kinesiology is destined to become an indispensable universal tool in health care in the years to come. We live in hazardous times which will get worse. Kinesiology will become a life preserving factor for millions of people.

KINESIOLOGY

IS

MUSCLE TESTING AND ENERGY BALANCING

WHAT CAN KINESIOLOGY DO?

It can help with more than 80% of all the health problems that most people put up with either because it isn't bad enough to go to the doctor, or they have sought help but received no relief.

Aches	Leg ache
Acne	Migraine
Allergies	Mood swings
Anxieties	Muscular Aches
Asthma	Neck ache
Backache	Nerves
Catarrh	Nervousness
Colds	Overweight
Depression	Pains
Diarrhoea	Paranoia
Digestive problems	Phobias
Dyslexia	Post Viral Syndrome
Elbow pain	Queasiness
Eczema	Restlessness
Energy lows	Sleep
Exhaustion	Smoking
Fatigue Fears	Sore shoulders
Flatulence	Stiff neck
Food sensitivies	Tennis elbow
Golfers Elbow	Tiredness
Headaches	Tummy trouble
Hip pain	Under weight
Indigestion	Vertigo
Jaw pain	Weight
Joint pain	X-Rays
Knee pain	Yeast
Learning problems	Zest for life.

POOR HEALTH IS PANDEMIC

Almost everyone you know suffers from one or other of this extensive list of conditions. None of them in themselves necessarily life threatening. They just make life a misery. Apparently 50% of all the people in this country suffer from back-ache at one time or another. Almost everyone gets Colds or the 'flu too often for comfort.

Just feeling "unwell" or "below par", or "a bit rough" seems almost to be the norm. It is accepted as a fact of life. It need not be! Kinesio-logy can help you balance your bodies' systems, and enjoy a level of health and well-being you may not have experienced since you were a child.

But why is everyone suffering from this multi-tude of problems? Previous centuries had their problems, but they were mostly to do with bad hygiene. Diseases like Cholera, Typhoid, and the Bubonic Plague and so on, are now almost a thing of the past in the West.

Our modern day problems are a different sort of plague. The causes of our present distresses are mainly due to our deteriorating environment, our hectic lifestyle, our eating habits, and our mostly non-existent exercise patterns. That list of ills is not caused by germs, but by the way we live.

HOW IS KINESIOLOGY DONE?

The person is asked to put their limbs in various specific positions. Each position tests a specific muscle. Each muscle is controlled by electrical circuits in the body.

The tester then asks the subject to hold the limb steady, while gentle pressure is exerted for two or three seconds. The pressure is then smoothly released.

If the muscle is "firing" correctly and contracts firmly and steadily, the limb will not move under the pressure. When this happens, the muscle and its controlling circuits are considered "balanced".

If the muscle is not firing correctly due to imbalances in the controlling circuits, the person will be unable to respond firmly, and the limb will move even under gentle pressure, or feel "spongy" to the tester. This is an indication that something is out of balance and needs correction

Imbalance may be because of an emotional disturbance, a nutritional lack, or for many reasons.

HOW ARE IMBALANCES CORRECTED?

There are many ways in Kinesiology in which imbalances may be corrected. In this book we are going to show just two of the most important.

Muscles rely on a good blood supply to work properly. Specific areas on the skull, called Neuro-Vascular points when contacted with the fingertips, enhance blood supply. A very light touch on these points for from twenty to thirty seconds can often enable a muscle to work better. They can also make the subject feel more relaxed and mentally clearer.

Although at first this might appear a very simple procedure, the effect of touching these points can be very profound. These reflexes were dis-covered in America by an Osteopath named Bennet.

In a later chapter we will explain how using these Neuro-Vascular points, you can help anyone to experience relief from emotional distress in a very simple yet very powerful way.

Muscles also need efficient feeding as they work. It is also vital to clean away the waste products. This is done by the bodies' lymphatic fluid which bathes the tissues with nourishment and cleans away the toxic waste. Lymphatic fluid mainly depends upon the movement of muscles to stimulate its efficient flow. It is not pumped like the blood is by the heart.

When lymphatic flow is inhibited, normal muscle function is impaired. The lymphatic reflexes are mostly on the body either side of the spine and the breastbone Firm massage on the lymphatic reflexes that relate to that muscle for about ten to twenty seconds, helps restore  balance to the lymphatic circuits. and strengthens the muscle.

These two correction methods form the basis of basic muscle balancing with Kinesiology. Good nutrition is also a vital factor. Different foods nourish different parts of the body. There are many other strengthening methods used by those who learn to use Kinesology professionally.

HOW DOES STRENGTHENING MUSCLES HELP PEOPLE OVERCOME PROBLEMS?

Our bodies are made up of Mental, Chemical, Physical and Energy components. These four aspects of a human being are totally involved and inter-related with each other. It is impossible to affect one without affecting all the others.

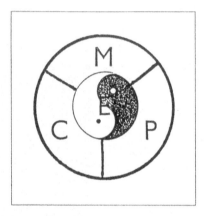

This diagram illustrates the four components. Anything that affects us adversely in the Mental realm, also has an effect upon our Energy, our Bio-chemistry, and our Physical body. Anything that hurts us Physically causes repercussions in the other realms, and this is true for each aspect.

When we rebalance muscles, we benefit the organs, other muscles, and even the mental state of the person. The energy released when muscles are balanced enhances all functions.

WHAT HAPPENS IF IMBALANCES ARE NOT CORRECTED AS THEY HAPPEN IN LIFE?

Some imbalances which occur in the course of every day living rectify themselves automatically. Those that do not, accumulate. The person's body has to compensate for the imbalance in one way or another. If the number of unresolved imbalances becomes too great for the body to adapt to, symptoms of one sort or another can occur. We are conditioned almost from birth to expect a steady decline in our state of health.

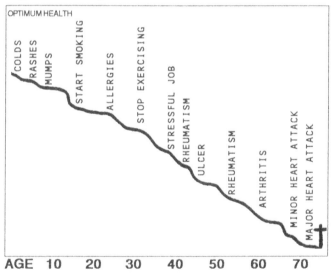

It is implied that life is a slippery slope of one debilitating thing after another which lead to an inevitable decline in well-being, and ultimately poor health and death.

Odd aches and pains, indigestion, tiredness, anxieties seem to become part of daily life. Most people accept the notion that the only solution apart from pain killers or pills is "to learn to live with it". Not always a satisfactory solution.

Ultimately, disease can occur if the bodies' need for restoration is neglected long enough. We do not "suddenly" get ill. Most acute problems are the result of years of unresolved chronic problems. Acute problems are hard to solve.

KINESIOLOGY HELPS PREVENTION!
The many imbalances which occur just coping with the stress of everyday life can be found, and then analysed with Kinesiology. All imbalances which can be found with Kinesiolology can be corrected. **Health and Well-Being improve.**

As we become healthier, our own miraculous powers of recuperation can get to work. Our bodies have many very intricate and amazing mechanisms for putting its own house in order. Just watch a cut heal!

By balancing imbalances regularly we help the body to solve the little problems. This means that big problems do not get a chance to develop. This opens the door to true *prevention.*

PREVENTION IS BETTER THAN CURE!
Thomas Edison, the inventor of the light bulb said over a hundred years ago:

> *The doctor of the future will give no medicines, but will interest his patients in the care of the human frame, in diet, and in the cause and **prevention** of disease.*

We are not quite there yet! But, with Kinesiology we now have the tools to deal with and correct the many day to day imbalances which the body is unable to resolve for itself.

KINESIOLOGY CAN HELP WITH OVER 80% OF ALL THE THINGS THAT TROUBLE PEOPLE THAT ARE NOT DISEASE

If you have a problem with any of the things listed on at the beginning of this section, there is a very good chance that Kinesiology will probably help you. Remember it is always wise to have a check-up with a health professional. Persistent problems should always be checked with a physician.

Kinesiology is simple, non-intrusive, and enables us to get into harmony with our own bodies. The basics are easy to learn and the results dramatic. Use the ideas in this book, and feel the benefit.

After you have used the muscle testing ideas in this book, and perhaps helped someone you love to feel better about a problem you may want to learn more. "Balanced Health" classes start with the simplest basics of Kinesiology, yet you will be surprised at what you can do after just a weekend. They suit everyone as no previous experience is necessary to get a real benefit.

In the Level I weekend class you can learn to help children (and adults) with reading and writing problems, The class is shown a very useful way to combat "brain fag" when studying or driving for long periods. Also a method is demonstrated which improves brain co-ordination which really helps those with dyslexic tendencies.

Participants learn to test for food sensitivities, and how any particular food or supplement is affecting the muscles. How the consumption of too little plain water, and too much coffee can aggravate or even cause backache!

Everyone enjoys the easy physical exercise which improves memory, poise, balance, especially when it is done to music. It is so easy to practice all you have learned at home, and the difference in well-being is very noticeable to the individual who benefits and also to others who see it.

THE ENVIRONMENT WE LIVE IN

There are holes in the Ozone Layer caused by using spray cans. The Ionosphere is scattered with space shot junk. Our atmosphere contains the radioactive particles of countless atomic explosions. Electromagnetic radiation from the tens of thousands of transmitters also affects us. Radar, radio, television and even telepones all radiate energy which is a stress to human beings.

The air is contaminated with vast amounts of burnt jet fuel, industrial waste gases, car exhaust fumes. Even the smoking of tobacco has been shown to affect not only those who smoke but also those who get it second hand.

These gases and contaminants affect us all adversely every time we breathe. This presents our bodies with a constant stress which is a drain on our energy and is debilitating.

The products of combustion include Carbon Dioxide which is the gas we breathe out after using the Oxygen to provide our life support. The level of Carbon Dioxide is rising fast due to the unprecented use of fuels on this earth. This gas is causing the temperature of the Earth to rise, although this has been disputed by scientists and politicians until very recently.

This temperature rise is upsetting world weather. It is disturbing the delicate balance of nature and the whole ecological system. If the ice caps melt, many of the the major cities of the world built on the sea fronts could be submerged. We have already experienced unprecedented upsets in global weather patterns.

OUR FOOD AND WATER

The polluting of our atmosphere is producing "acid rain" which ruins crops. Our food is being grown with the use of artificial chemicals. Many fertilisers and pest control chemicals poison the soil. They kill off the worms, and the natural organisms of the earth which would otherwise be keeping the soil in good heart.

Foods grown with these unnatural processes are deficient in the very nutrients we need to be healthy. Vegetables contain a fraction of the vital mineral content they did sixty years ago. They look fine on the supermarket shelves, but in many cases have little to nourish us.

Farmers are feeding animal meat and animal waste to herbivorous animals. Cows and Sheep do not eat meat naturally. Forcing them to do so is producing its own devastating diseases. Notice that the discussion on B.S.E. or mad cow disease does not usually address the way the animals are fed, but how to kill off the disease by breeding or burning the heads when they are killed!

The animals we eat are also being fed drugs to make them grow faster, and to keep them from dying from disease which they would otherwise fall prey to because of the way they are managed.

Foods are processed, irradiated, preserved with yet more chemicals, and then presented to us in an attractive packet. Not all the ingredients are listed on the label. No matter how careful you are in selecting your food, it can contain things which are not declared on the list of contents.

We are the unwitting subjects of the biggest un-controlled experiment in human nutrition ever conducted. What the results will be, no one knows because it has never been tried before!

EXERCISE

Over the last sixty years, the number of people involved with manual labour has diminished dramatically. There has been a mass migration from the land and industry to offices and other relatively sedentary jobs. Insufficient exercise could well prove to be more of a cause of heart disease than cholesterol ever was.

OUR MENTAL DIET
Human beings have never lived under such bad conditions. The constant threat of nuclear war, the population explosion, the breakdown of the eco-system may not dominate everyone's consciousness, but they certainly affect us mentally.

Anxieties, worries, fears and phobias abound and reduce our effectiveness as a nation. The lack of proper nutrients in our foods leave our nervous systems depleted of the very things we need to cope with the mental strain of a hectic, busy, rushed and stress-filled lifestyle.

IS IT ANY WONDER WE ARE SICK?

KINESIOLOGY CAN REALLY HELP!
Depressed? Don't be, Although we cannot escape entirely from the results of man's reckless treatment of our Earth Mother, Kinesiology does provide many ways to help us cope better with the situation as it exists while working for change

We can use techniques which really do relieve mental stress and anxiety. There are specific things you can do to help you feed and nourish your body better. There are even simple exercises to help you improve your physical and mental fitness without the burn!!

KINESIOLOGY - A WHOLISTIC APPROACH
Kinesiology offers many ways to help the whole person. Any health care approach which neglects to deal with all four specific aspects of human function will not be as effective. The four components of a human being are:

1. THE MENTAL/EMOTIONAL REALM

2. DIETARY AND CHEMICAL FACTORS

3. STRUCTURAL CONSIDERATIONS

4. LIFE FORCE ENERGY IMBALANCES

Every ailment or condition experienced by anyone has a **mental** component, **bio-chemical** factors, **musculo-skeletal** compensations, and **energy** disturbances. In Kinesiology each one is addressed, and any imbalances corrected. We will look at each in turn for a moment.

1. THE MENTAL/EMOTIONAL REALM
The way we think, the way we use our emotions affects our bodies much more than we realise. The mind has an immediate and continuous effect upon the body, either for good or ill. The word *psychosomatic* literally means the real effect the mind has on the body.

Wrong thinking can, and does produce symptoms and pains which are real. They are very real indeed to those who suffer from them, despite being told that "it is all in the mind". It is not all in the mind. It is in the body too. We cannot separate one from the other!

Shock, disappointments, arguments, depression, all have an instantaneous effect on us. The tests used in Kinesiology show dramatically just how upset emotions disorientate the energy of the body and its ability to function at its best. This effect may be demonstrated by the way they change a muscle's ability to contract normally.

If unresolved, the build-up of mental stress can greatly influence the onset, duration and severity of disease processes. It may drastically affect a person's ability to recover to robust health also.

So often we feel rather helpless when confronted by someone who is really upset. Making a cup of tea, or a consoling arm around their shoulders does not always provide the relief we might wish.

The gentle caring you can provide by utilising the simple method of Emotional Stress Relief you will read about in a later chapter, really has to be experienced to be believed.

In just a few minutes, people can come to terms with even deep traumas. They can quickly feel free of worry, stress or anxiety over any given matter. All it takes is for someone to place their fingers on the appropriate points for a while. This can be very rewarding for the one offering to help.

2. DIETARY AND CHEMICAL FACTORS

Secondly, the effect of diet is of vital importance. Food can either be a creative and supportive force, or very destructive. We either injest needed vital nutrients which are absorbed by the body and increase our vitality, or we can slowly but surely poison ourselves.

Many people eat foods which actually feed the health problems they suffer from, for instance, those who suffer from Candida Albicans, and other fungal infections. Many of us consume foods based on our personal preferences, regardless of whether they are giving us energy, or taking it away, as some foods can do.

It is now being dramatically demonstrated daily in clinics up and down the country that "wholesome crusty stone-ground organic wholemeal bread" affects some people very adversely indeed! And yet for others it is the staff of life.

We are now being forced to realise the wisdom of taking into account biochemic individuality. It is vital for each person to adjust their diet to that which suits them individually.

There are foods, which for some people, take more energy than they give to the body. This is more easily observed in cases where someone has an allergy. It is rather less obvious when it is just not nourishing the person. Food testing using Kinesiological muscle tests may effectively be used to discover the hidden detrimental effects of foods unsuitable for any particular individual.

DRUGS AND CHEMICALS
Virtually all drugs have undesirable side effects. This does not mean they should not be used, merely that their use should be prescribed as conservatively as possible.

An important factor in the health of anyone is the state of the millions of friendly bacteria which live in our intestines. The widespread use of anti-biotics for minor health problems is now causing havoc in the intestinal flora of the nation.

The results are highly unfortunate. When it is necessary to use these potent killers, then some post medicative attention to correct the ensuing bowel imbalances would save a fortune in anti-depressants and a mountain of human misery.

We are enmeshed in the largest uncontrolled experiment in human nutrition ever conducted. More chemicals, preservatives, colourings, and additives are being used by the food industry in the preparation of our "foods" than ever before.

The long term effects of this upon our own health, and that of our children cannot be known. It is certainly best to avoid as far as possible all manufactured foods.

Give greater emphasis to fish, vegetables and grains which we prepare ourselves. Unhappily though, these too are not completely untainted from the effects of sprays and fertilizers. If the vegetables are first washed thoroughly, it helps to reduce the dangers of accumulated poisons building up in the body.

3. STRUCTURAL INTEGRITY
The care of the human frame must include regular exercise, and the careful avoidance of accidental damage. Many people who work hard all day and get very tired, think that they get sufficient exercise. This is not always true.

The heart is a muscle just like others in the body and needs exercise. For exercise to be of real value the heart rate needs to be increased to twice its normal resting rate, or whatever rate a doctor advises in the case of anyone who is really unfit. *Failure to get advice upon the most appropriate exercise regime accounts for many deaths each year.* Please exercise with caution if you have not exercised for a long time.

These events are frequently used by the media to "prove" the dangers of exercising. One is often led to wonder whether the journalists who write these scare stories get their exercise from jumping to conclusions, operating cigarette lighters, or gently raising large gin and tonics to the lips.

The truth of the matter is, that if one takes regular exercise to produce the desired increase in heart rate, it involves some deep breathing and production of some healthy sweat three or four times a week. Do this, and the chances of ever dying from a heart attack are greatly reduced.

Applied Kinesiology helps greatly in restoring postural integrity in those who have muscular tension. As the muscle imbalances are corrected, posture is improved, and a sense of ease and grace returns to body movements.

4. ENERGY AND LIFE FORCE.

Possibly most important of all, Kinesiology can address many of the body's electrical imbalances in a way which has never been before possible. Acupuncture deals with energies on a deep level, magnets can also move energies to great effect.

In the orthodox approach to most training in Western medicine, the existence of the life-force energy pathways, known to acupuncturists of the Orient for five thousand years, is not yet even considered. Happily there has been increasing interest by the medical profession in recent years in the concepts and practice of acupuncture.

Knowing about the energy flows greatly improves our ability to help the sick, especially when this knowledge is used in conjunction with other modalities. When the life force energies are well balanced, the individual feels the beneficial effect immediately, in some relief, and an enhanced sense of well being is experienced even though the person may be unwell or in pain.

Kinesiological muscle testing can reveal where the 'bio-computers' which control all bodily functions at an electro-magnetic level are out of tune. In a very similar way to the motor car, if the electrical ignition system is out of tune, the mechanical parts of the car cannot run properly. It is the same with the human body.

KINESIOLOGY REALLY DOES ADDRESS AND REBALANCE THE WHOLE PERSON

Kinesiology, properly used, is capable of being the most wholistic approach to natural health care. Practitioners from all branches of both orthodox and complementary medicine are finding Kinesiology an indispensable tool to supplement and augment their own skills they have learned within their own discipline.

Since Kinesiology rebalances and revitalises the major systems of the body, it enhances internal natural healing processes. Kinesiologists do not address disease, nor attempt cures of pathology. Some say their job is to make the good bits work better, and in so doing the body is facilitated to return to health.

KINESIOLOGICAL MUSCLE TESTING

Muscle testing is the way Kinesiologists "read" the body. Muscle response to light pressure for a few seconds can reveal a lot about a person. How can a muscle test tell us so much? The body, mind, organs, are an interconnected whole.

This section is going to explain how to perform the basic muscle test. It is really very simple, and like anything one learns that requires touch, practice makes for increased skill.

Let us start by putting on record how NOT to go about testing muscles. There are only five **DON'TS** to remember when muscle testing.

1. **DON'T** coerce people into being tested, or play with muscle testing, it is not a game.

2. **DON'T** you or the subject hold your breath.

3. **DON'T** apply pressure too quickly as it will produce an incorrect result.

4. **DON'T** push too hard, it is NOT a trial of strength. Use only about 4-10lbs of pressure.

5. **DON'T** push for too long, it simply tires any muscle. Two or three seconds is long enough.

These five DON'TS come first because we want you to be successful in your testing right from the start. Please, please, only attempt muscle testing with someone who is really WILLING. Always first obtain their permission. Many people have broken this rule and regretted it deeply.

Remember: "*Anyone who is convinced against their will, is of the same opinion still.*"

Ignoring this warning often results in serious disappointment, incorrect results, ridicule, and everything you do not want to experience whilst learning and using Kinesiological testing .

BASIC MUSCLE TESTING PROCEDURE
Muscle testing is a very simple procedure, easily learned. Testing is such a valuable tool, you will want to get correct results. To get the best re-sults, follow these guidelines very carefully each time you do a test.

1. ASK PERMISSION.
Be sure that the person you want to test is really willing and not just going along with it to please you.

2. BOTH PARTIES **BREATHE NORMALLY**
There is a tendency to hold one's breath when

testing. The tester holds their breath because they are concentrating. The subject tends to hold their breath at the crucial moment when they are resisting the pressure. Most of us stop breathing momentarily when we exert ourselves. So KEEP BREATHING.

3. SLOWLY APPLY GENTLE PRESSURE

Once the person has put their limb into the exact starting position with your help, indicate the direction you will be applying the pressure, say "HOLD", pause a moment for them to respond, then apply the pressure slowly until you feel the limb "lock" into place as their muscle "fires", or you feel it feels "spongy" or the limb begins to give way.

4. USE ONLY GENTLE PRESSURE.

Remember that muscle testing is not a trial of strength, but a gentle assessment of function. Light pressure will often work better than firm.

5. BRIEFLY PUSH FOR ONLY TWO OR THREE SECONDS.

Muscles are designed to work for brief periods and then switch off. Recognising this, sustained pressure for anything over a few seconds will quickly tire the muscle, it will seem to be weak when it is not, and the test will not be accurate.

THE TESTING PROCEDURE FOR THE PECTORALIS MAJOR CLAVICULAR

Muscles are called by Latin names which help to define where they are on the body. Although we do not speak Latin today, these terms are used universally by the medical and sports professions, and so we use them.

The first muscle test we are going to explain is the Pectoralis Major Clavicular (P.M.C.). The Pectoral muscles are the muscles of the upper chest. The P.M.C. as this muscle is called for short, originates along the clavicle or collar bone. The muscle goes across the chest, crosses the shoulder joint and inserts into the bone at the top of the arm.

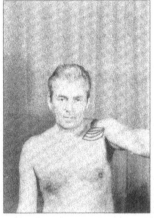

The job of this muscle is to raise the arm from the relaxed position by the side up and towards the centre line of the body. It is related to the Stomach Meridian, foods and emotions.

In Kinesiology, the starting position for each specific muscle test involves putting the limb into the position where the muscle is contracted. The limb is then held in the position with the muscle contracted while the test takes place.

The starting position for the Pectoralis Major Clavicular test is with the arm held at right angles to the shoulders, parallel to the floor, with the hand turned so that the thumb is pointing downwards.

Pressure is applied by the tester to the inside of the wrist to press the arm downwards and away from the body as shown. Remember that when the muscle is firing correctly, the arm will remain stable under pressure and will not move at all when tested.

This muscle test is invaluable to assess reactions to certain foods as well as to determine response to emotional stress and traumas.

The second test is for the Supraspinatus muscle.

Supra means above, and spinatus means spine. In this case the spine is a ridge of bone at the top of the shoulder blade. This muscle is connected to the Central Meridian, and is related to the Brain. It is a useful test to check for brain fatigue and learning difficulties.

The starting position is with the arm raised away from the body about fifteen degrees up and about thirty degrees out to the side of the body. Pressure is against the wrist to press the arm towards the groin in the centre of the body.

This muscle is also a good indicator for people with dyslexic tendencies. Strengthening this muscle whilst thinking in relation to particular problems will often help in their resolution.

The third muscle is called the Latissimus Dorsii. This is a large muscle in the back which is controlled by the Spleen Meridian, and is related to the Pancreas.

In the starting position for the Latissimus Dorsii, the palm is turned out, and the elbow is kept straight, and the arm is held into the side. The tester slips their fingers in between the wrist and the body and pressure is exerted to attempt to draw the arm away from the side.

This book is designed simply to provide an introduction to Kinesiology. We have only shown three muscle tests, but they will get you started on an exciting journey. These muscle tests will enable you to get some meaningful results when you use them as described in the next section.

If you want to learn more muscle tests there are Instructors all over the country who hold Basic Classes in Systematic Kinesiology who will give you a warm welcome in their classes.

WHAT IF THE MUSCLE DOES NOT TEST STRONGLY, FEELS "SPONGY" OR WEAK?

The first correction contact points to try are the Neuro-Vascular points which enhance the blood supply to the muscle and to the related organ.

The Neuro-Vascular Contact points, which are located on the head, and need only the lightest touch for thirty to sixty seconds to balance the circuit and strengthen the related muscle.

The Neuro-Vascular points for:

The Supraspinatus
Frontal Eminences and the Anterior Fontanel

The Pectoralis Major Clavicular, or P.M.C.
The frontal eminences.

The Latissimus Dorsii
One inch above, and slightly behind the centre of the ear.

Contact these points with the pads of your fingertips. Only contact with sufficient pressure to prevent slipping off the point. Touch for about 30-60 seconds. Then retest the muscle to see if there is any change in its response to light pressure. If the Neuro-Vascular point was relevant to its previous weakness, it will strengthen.

The Neuro-Lymphatic Massage correction points are located on the body . They require a fairly firm type of massage, and may be quite tender to touch. These need to be rubbed for about twenty to thirty seconds.

Do not apply any more pressure than the person can reasonably tolerate. It is alright for them to be uncomfortable, but not painful. This slight discomfort will diminish as you work on them. If the discomfort increases a lot, stop rubbing.

Front Neuro-Lymphatic points: Supraspinatus:
An arc just inside and around the front of the shoulder joint.

The P.M.C.
An arc under the left breast between the 5th & 6th ribs.

The Latissimus Dorsii:
In a hollow between the 7th & 8th ribs where ribs curve.

Back Neuro-Lymphatic points: Supraspinatus:
Just under the skull either side of the neck vertebrae.

The P.M.C.
An inch or so either side of spine between 5th & 6th ribs.

The Latissimus Dorsii
An inch or so either side of spine between 7th & 8th ribs.

WHAT IF NONE OF THESE POINTS STRENGTHENS THE MUSCLE?

There is nothing to be concerned about. Muscles can be turned off for many reasons. There are other ways to correct muscles which we have not dealt with in this introduction to Kinesiology. Other strengthening methods are taught in the classes to those who are studying Kinesiology in more depth.

It will be unusual if all three muscles test weak. It will also be unlikely that you will not be able to strengthen one or another with the points given.

If after using the correction points, the muscles still test weak, check that you are not pushing too quickly or too hard, or for too long.

If they still test weak, you may want to contact the person from whom you obtained this book, or contact the Association for the name of someone who uses Kinesiology locally to you.

Sometimes people are tempted to think that maybe Kinesiology does not work. It always "works". It is just that sometimes when we get results that we did not expect, we forget that there may be other factors at work of which we are unaware.

EMOTIONAL STRESS RELEASE (E.S.R.)
One of the simplest of Kinesiological techniques can help relieve upset feelings in a very powerful way. Emotional Stress Release (E.S.R.) really can work wonders.

How many times have you wanted to reach out and help someone who is very upset? Have you felt a bit helpless sometimes? Tea and sympathy certainly have their place, as does a consoling arm around the shoulder and a listening ear. But unfortunately these sympathetic and kindly acts do not always really help in a permanent way.

Everyone has to contend in daily life with events and circumstances which create negative feelings. Keeping calm and centred at times of emotional upsets is not easy. We all experience emotional stress in our lives. It affects us all adversely at one time or another. Kinesiology offers a way to help others resolve upsets simply.

Despite all out efforts to keep smiling, life's trials and tribulations sometimes get us down.

When we are knocked off our emotional equilibrium, everything seems more difficult to handle. Unpleasant jobs we would normally tackle easily seem daunting. Difficult people we can normally cope with suddenly become impossible to contend with. Work stresses we can usually handle, cause us to fly off it!

It does not seem to matter how serious the problem appears at the time, using E.S.R. will help the person deal with it. A few minutes of this hands on method of dealing with upset feelings will create an entirely new perspective. The amazing thing is that the relief gained seems to be permanent.

E.S.R. HELPS DEAL WITH OVERWHELM
When the mounting stressors involve excess input, "too much to do" or "too many things at once" people can develop feelings of confusion and being "unable to cope". We can get overwhelmed by the sheer amount of things we have to deal with. This state of overwhelm can be greatly relieved with the Emotional Stress Release technique.

WHAT HAPPENS TO US WHEN WE ARE OVER STRESSED AND OVERWHELMED?
Under excessive stress the blood supply to the left and right hemispheres of the brain can become unbalanced. When increasing stress induces fear, the thinking part of the brain is "paralysed". Under acute stress, the body

engages its automatic "fight/flight" mechanism. All the body's resources are focussed on dealing with the crisis. Clear objective thinking goes out of the window until the crisis is dealt with.

Regrettably our ability to reason and think can be clouded for long periods if the stresses are not resolved.

Wouldn't it be wonderful to have a practical way to help yourself, your friends, relatives and colleagues to cope better with distress?

E.S.R., a simple, yet very powerful technique will help anyone face a problem no matter how serious. Most people can gain almost immediate relief from the anguish they may be suffering. Nothing could be simpler to do, for it is merely the extension of a natural gesture.

HOW E.S.R. WAS DISCOVERED

A research Kinesiologist used to working with emotionally distressed people, one day noticed that there is a common physical reaction to being emotionally distressed.

People put their hands to their foreheads automatically when faced with a situation that is hard for them to deal with emotionally. It is only a momentary gesture, but as soon as the stress gets difficult to handle, the hand covers the brow. He wondered if this example of body language was telling him something he could use in practice.

He also noticed that when his clients were very upset and began to be tearful, then they would cover their faces with their palms. With both hands in this position, their fingertips rested naturally on the two mounds on the forehead in a vertical line above the centre of the iris of the eye. These two mounds are called the 'frontal eminences'.

The natural gesture people make of touching the forehead is usually very brief, only lasting a few seconds. Perhaps this reflects our tendency to run away from problems rather than face them. When confronted with life's upsetting issues we may try to think of something else, or in some way avoid them, and hope they will go away.

If we do actually set out to think the problem

through whilst upset, it just seems to get worse and worse as we go round in circles. The secret of using E.S.R. effectively is to force oneself, or strongly urge your friend, to concentrate on the main core of the problem for as long as possible. The miracle is that the harder one tries to focus on the problem, the harder it gets to do so.

Researchers found that the best results were obtained when the distressed individual had the contact maintained with the forehead for at least a minute or two. Sometimes up to even ten or fifteen minutes contact were required before relief was obtained. Especially if the problem was serious, deep seated, or complex in nature.

As soon as his clients gave signs of being upset, he began to touch their foreheads very lightly with his fingertips whilst encouraging them to continue to feel the emotions related to the problem.

To his astonishment, he found there was an almost universal response to this form of treatment. Nearly everyone expressed surprise that after only a minute or two, the problem now seemed to be of less stress or importance. In many cases the person couldn't understand what they were worrying about it for in the first place!

NEW SOLUTIONS TO OLD PROBLEMS

On other occasions, individuals would volunteer that the possibility of a new solution had now occurred to them which they had not thought of before. This is because touching the forehead in this manner brings blood to the frontal lobes of the brain. The more blood in the brain the clearer the thinking becomes. The frontal lobes deal with new possibilities, new ideas and concepts.

Emotional disturbances are intimately linked with the stomach. When someone is upset, the stomach meridian is frequently disturbed. Touching these points on the frontal eminences may also help balance the energy in the stomach meridian, which has an additonal calming effect.

Although all this may seem too good to be true, it works. This procedure helps the subject to face a problem no matter how serious it might be. Most people gain almost immediate relief. It is virtually impossible for a person to remain emotionally upset whilst this is being done.

The wonderful bonus is that the effect of using E.S.R. is permanent. Whatever was upsetting that person, the aspect they dealt with using E.S.R. will never trouble them again to the same extent or degree.

A-Z BENEFITS OF USING E.S.R. POINTS

These heading have been suggested by people who have experienced relief or help in the particular areas listed, and there are many more.

Actors, learn lines easier.
After accidents Resets Switches
Aligns Conscious/Subconscious
Athletics, improve performance.
Building and Improving Skills
Caring for others
Creating Solutions
Diet anxieties relieved
Digestion Improves
Digestive disorders
Dissolves Old Memories
Drug rehabilitation
Eases Anxieties
Emotional Balance
Emotional problems resolved
Empathy for self and others
Enhances Well-Being
Examination Nerves banished
Exams passed
Face Problems - with confidence
Facilitates "Imagineering"
Fears unknown disappear
Fears known faced
Finding things that are lost
Flexible, no set way or time.
Fosters Trust In Others
Fractures and accident pains
Future worries
Grief relieved
Handling Overwhelm
Helps balance R/L Brain
Helps in Dieting.
Immediacy, use at any time

Injuries, current
Injuries, old
Learning Skills improve
Memory enhancement
Memories, erasing effects of
Money worries eased
Mugging victims
No equipment needed
No Training Required
Old Injuries
"Overwhelm" handled better
Past Traumas
Personal problems diminish
Phobias banished
Post Operative Trauma
Positive "imagineering" with ESR
Practical way to be Caring
Pre-Operative fears.
Privacy can be maintained.
Problem solving
Promotes trust.
Pulled muscles
Rape victims
Reciprocal, to help each other.
Relationship Stresses
Relieves Sub-Conscious fears.
Resets Switches After Accidents
R/L Brain Hemispheres Balance
Self-Determining
Simple to do.
Sub-Conscious Fears
Tension released
Unknown Fears
Well Being enhanced
Wipe old "tapes"
Zeal and Zest for life.

No doubt as you use E.S.R., you will find things
special to you, where you will find special benefit

HOW TO USE THE E.S.R. TECHNIQUE

If you want to help yourself, or someone else handle a problem, first get yourself into a comfortable position which you will be able to maintain for a few minutes.

It works best when the two mounds immediately above the iris, about halfway between the eyebrows and the person's original hairline, are contacted with a very gentle touch. Place the tips of your fingers on them with the lightest possible pressure.

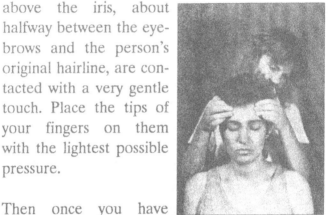

Then once you have made contact stretch the skin a millimetre or two upwards towards the hairline. Maintain a steady light pressure until the person feels relieved. Only touch with just sufficient contact that you do not slip off the brow as you stretch the skin slightly upwards toward the hairline.

ENHANCES BLOOD SUPPLY TO BRAIN

Contacting these points also stimulates and balances the blood supply to the whole of the brain. The brain uses up over twenty percent of all the oxygen we breath. As the blood supply is normalised by this technique, it helps the brain attain its optimum working conditions. A healthy blood supply is vital to think clearly.

You can certainly do it to yourself. If one wants to maintain contact with one's own forehead, this will certainly have a beneficial effect. One can either use the finger-tips of both hands, or cover the brow with the palm. However, there is definitely an increased 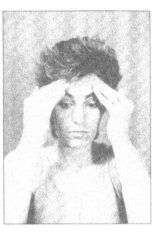 effectiveness when it is done by another person who wants to help you resolve your problem.

This is especially true when the problem is multi-facetted. Help the person through it by suggesting they deal with one specific aspect at a time. Have them choose the most acutely distressing point first, and then go on to other areas.

PRIVACY AND CONFIDENTIALITY.
It is a priviledge to be invited to help another with their problems. Privacy is one of the most important advantages of using E.S.R.

The person does not have to verbalise the nature of the problem they are dealing with. They do not have to explain verbally what it is they are concerned about. If they want to, that is fine. However, it is often easier to visualise a problem than to explain it.

This non-invasive aspect of E.S.R. is of vital importance. It enables one to be of practical help in areas of people's lives which are totally private to them and they wish to keep it that way. If that is how they feel then that is to be completely respected.

Confidentiality is especially useful in dealing with children and their problems. They often do not want to talk about them, but they will let you help in this supportive, but non-intrusive way.

FOCUS HARD ON THE PROBLEM
It is important for you, or for the person you are helping to concentrate hard on the core of the problem no matter how painful or upsetting this may be. So long as you keep your fingertips on the forehead, the pain, distress and hurt will just melt away in a matter of minutes.

Encourage the subject to focus on the image of a single aspect of the problem and not several, whilst they are being touched. It is essential for the person to keep on focussing on the core of the problem, even if it tends to fade away, which it usually does.

Most problems have many different aspects, each of which can create a different type of distress. It is important for the person to dwell on the same point until it no longer generates anxiety or causes distress. Then other aspects of the same problem may be dealt with as they come up.

Our minds have a built in priority system which only allows us to think about one thing at a time. The most significant anxiety is the one which dominates our thinking. As soon as that is relieved, the next in importance surfaces in our consciousness.

Have them choose the most acutely distressing point first. It is certainly more effective that way. Depending upon the nature of the problem, you may find it could take from two, and up to twenty minutes to give relief.

WHAT IS THE RESULT OF USING E.S.R.?
This simple technique is very powerful. It always works. It always helps the person. The most usual reaction is for the person to tell you that,

"it doesn't seem to matter so much" or "I just cannot seem to worry about it any more". The sharp sting goes out of painful problems. It really does help to get problems into perspective.

It can be used to help give relief to people suffering from phobias of flying, spiders, heights and so on. Anxieties about future events,and past problems may all be effectively addressed. The E.S.R. technique may be used at any time, and under any circumstances.

MUSCLE TESTING - A LANGUAGE
Muscle testing before, during and after using E.S.R. can increase its effectiveness. Muscle testing is a language. It is a way to communicate with the body on all levels. When a muscle is tested, and the limb gives way, this is recorded in the persona mentally, chemically, and physically.

When using muscle testing in connection with E.S.R., it has a powerful "anchoring" effect. It confirms to the person in a physical way that something positive has happened mentally.

USING MUSCLE TESTING WITH E.S.R.
Most emotional problems affect the Stomach. The pectoralis major clavicular (P.M.C.) muscle is related to the stomach meridian. It is also

related to the stomach itself, so it is a good muscle to use in connection with emotions.

Testing the P.M.C. is a good way to check whether the subject is really in touch with the unpleasant emotion. If they are not really in touch with the feeling the arm will remain strong.

THE PROCEDURE IS SIMPLE:

1. Ask the person you are testing to raise their arm into the testing position, and think of some neutral subject while you test the muscle. Ask them to look at the trees outside the window, or think about the blue sky or a nice beach. The P.M.C. should test strong. If it does not, use the Neuro-Vascular points or the Neuro-Lymphatic correcting points to get the muscle testing strong.

2. Then have your subject dwell on the most upsetting aspect of their problem either silently to themselves, or verbally, or a mixture of the two. Go by what they feel is appropriate.

3. Whilst they are thinking of the disturbing issue, have them raise their arm again, and allow you to test it. If they have the upsetting thought clearly enough to mind, the muscle will "unlock" and the arm will go down.

4. As soon as this happens, place you fingers on the Frontal Eminences, slightly stretch the skin towards the hairline, hold your fingers steady and verbally encourage the subject to continue to concentrate on the core of the problem and not wander off it.

5. After a minute or two, or three or four, one of several things will happen. The person may sigh, or give signs of obvious relaxation. They may express difficulty in holding the thought in mind. They may say the problem does not seem so bad as it did, or in some way express relief.

6. Ask them to raise their arm again, concentrate on the exact same aspect of the problem they were just concentrating on, and carefully retest the muscle.

If the thought is defused, the arm will remain strong. If it still tests weak, this indicates there is more to do, so repeat the procedure starting at point 2.

7. Keep going through the procedure either until thinking about any aspect or facet of the problem no longer weakens the pectoralis major clavicular muscle, or the person feels that they would like to stop.

It is not essential to test the muscle before dealing with problems in this way, but it does make the procedure more effective. It emphasises the body/mind language communication which is the factor which makes Kinesiology so very effective.

It also "anchors" the fact of the beneficial changes that have taken place more firmly in the person's body/mind. This reinforces the fact that the body can now contend with the issues involved without it being weakening.

No other way of dealing with emotional issues is as effective as using all the tools which are available to those who practice Kinesiology. Psychotherapy, hypnotherapy, and counselling are all effective, but qualified therapists trained in these forms of treatment find Kinesiology helps them get results more effectively, and faster too.

HOW IS KINESIOLOGY DONE?

The person is asked to put their limbs in various specific positions. Each position tests a specific muscle. Each muscle is controlled by electrical circuits in the body.

The tester then asks the subject to hold the limb steady, while gentle pressure is exerted for two or three seconds. The pressure is then smoothly released.

If the muscle is "firing" correctly and contracts firmly and steadily, the limb will not move under the pressure. When this happens, the muscle and its controlling circuits are considered "balanced".

If the muscle is not firing correctly due to imbalances in the controlling circuits, the person will be unable to respond firmly, and the limb will move even under gentle pressure, or feel "spongy" to the tester. This is an indication that something is out of balance and needs correction

Imbalance may be because of an emotional disturbance, a nutritional lack, or for many reasons.

the back of the head where we actually "see" what we see.

This often speeds up the process of releasing mental anxiety, as well as opening up new possibilities for the subject to solve old problems. It also balances left/right front/back brain functions, by increasing electrical field energy flow as well as enhancing blood circulation.

It can also help to have the person reassume the position they were in at the time of the trauma, whilst this procedure and other types of emotional stress clearing are used. Maybe they fell off a horse. Which part of them hit the ground first? In car accidents, whiplash is always a factor. What was their position at the moment of impact when the car stopped?

Emotional stress release, dealing with fears and phobias, and other psychological problems is a big subject which is covered in depth in some of the classes offered by the Academy of Systematic Kinesiology.

If this subject interests you particularly, then the tools available to those who study Kinesiology in depth enable remarkable work to be done in the resolution of emotional pain and traumas.

THE ORIGINS OF KINESIOLOGY

The discovery and development of Kinesiology is a fascinating story. It is a mixture of serendipity, painstaking determination, research genius and a great deal of hard work on the part of hundreds of clinicians.

Chiropractors and Osteopaths have provided an alternative way to approach to health care for over a hundred years. These formal names now dignify those highly trained, whose predecessors were "bonesetters" or natural manipulators with no formal training or qualification whatsoever.

The healing power of herbs and plants have been used since time began. In the East, over five thousand years of acupuncture attest to yet other amazing ways of man's ability to help his fellow man gain relief from pain and enjoy better health. Applied Kinesiology draws these and many more disciplines together to provide a systematic method of analysing and treating a very wide range of conditions.

In 1964, Dr. George Goodheart, a chiropractor from Michigan, was already a leader in his profession. He was well known in the chiropractic world for his seminars on new techniques. One day he made a unique observation which was to lead him on an exciting journey of discovery, and open up a whole new world of possibilities.

Many stories abound as to how it all began. One version suggests that he was doing his best to help a patient referred to him by colleague who had been quite unable to give the poor man relief from his pain. As Dr. Goodheart made his examination, he found some severe muscle spasm. He decided to use some muscle testing procedures used by kinesiologists to determine function.

One of the muscles he tested was the Fascia Lata, which runs down the outside of the leg from the hip to just below the knee. He massaged the path of the muscle, and the patient commented that the pain was diminishing dramatically, the first relief he had had in a long search for help! Dr. Goodheart retested the Fascia Lata muscle to find that its response to being tested was much stronger than before.

Encouraged by this phenomenon, Dr. Goodheart proceeded to massage the fibres of other muscles, but was intrigued that the same result was not forthcoming. He then recalled that some work on lymph had been done by an osteopath called Chapman at the turn of the century.

Chapman has mapped reflexes which he had demonstrated improved the flow of lymph. Lymph is the fluid that feeds and cleans the tissues of the body where the blood does not reach.

Whilst reading Chapman's work, he noticed that one of the reflexes followed the path of the Fascia Lata muscle. He wondered if this was what had strengthened the muscle. It turned out that this reflex was the only one which was over the muscle it affected. This caused him step by step, to match the rest of the points discovered by Chapman, with the muscles to which they related.

These are now know as the "Neuro-lymphatic" reflexes of Applied Kinesiology, a new science born out of the perseverence of Dr. Goodheart. "Neuro-" because a term was needed to explain the immediate effect they have when activated. One could call them "Electro-lymphatic" switches for they work so quickly. Weak muscles become strong within a few seconds if one cause for their weakness is principally a mis-firing of what now seems to be an electrical circuit.

Lymph feeds and cleans the inter-cellular spaces, and is vital to healthy function. Certainly the medical profession would say it is impossible to explain physiologically how a change in the lymphatic flow could be stimulated by massaging a point. Nor explain how this is able instantly to improve a muscle's ability to perform so dramatically in such a short time. However, the fact remains that they do.

Thousands use these reflexes on a daily basis in their clinical work, as do people who have taken the lay classes use them in the home to tremendous effect. As Dr. Goodheart's research continued, and gained in acceptance he soon had a number of his colleagues checking his findings and adding to them.

His next breakthrough was to correlate the blood circulation enhancing reflexes of Bennet with the muscles to which they relatedthey strengthened. Bennet, an Osteopath, had discovered that the circulation of the various organs could be enhanced merely by touching lightly certain points on the skull.

He used a "Fluoroscope" a kind of movie X-ray machine for his research. This regrettably gave off a lot of very harmful radiation, which probably accounted for his early death from cancer. This led to some more interesting connections being made in body circuitry. Now some of the relationships between the musculature and the organs which share a common energy pathway were becoming clearer. Some of these pathways may be understood in relation to the orthodox approach to physiology, others cannot. Nevertheless, they exist.

The next huge jump forward in Kinesiology occurred when the connection was made between the ancient oriental concepts of life force or 'chi, the pathways of energy called meridians, and the muscles of the body.

These meridians, each with points along their length where traditional acupuncturists insert their needles, were understood to be related to the internal organs. Kinesiological research had made the vital connection between these energy pathways and the muscles.

Since that time, Kinesiology continues to grow by leaps and bounds. Many skilled professionals add their freshly researched and checked new techniques to the body of knowledge now called Kinesiology each year. This information is passed on to many thousands of interested students all around the world in seminars for the professionals and classes for lay people.

IN CONCLUSION

This short book affords merely a brief glimpse into the world of Kinesiology. Muscle testing allows us to examine all aspects of the human being without intrusion. The power it offers even to lay people who take just a weekend course is phenomenal.

Many professional therapists, doctors, dentists, and physiotherapists have exclaimed with some amazement that they learned more of practical value in two days than in two years of formal orthodox education. One doctor was almost tearful at the thought of how much help she could have given to so many people with just the tool of E.S.R., had she not just retired.

The only value of information is as it is put to use. You now have one of the most powerful, yet simple tools available to you. It did not take months to learn, or cost a fortune in fees. Do not let this allow you to devalue it, or fail to use it.

Once you have helped some of your family, your friends and aquaintances, you will recognise the enormous power you have at your fingertips.

Take time to learn more. In the hazardous days ahead, Kinesiology will prove invaluable to you.

Many people's lives have been transformed by learning to use Kinesiology. The techniques learned in one particular part of the Certificate course, the Advanced Communications Training Workshop, (T.A.C.T.) have been a turning point in the lives of dozens of individuals. Marriages saved, relationships with children improved, work situations resolved, creating a new era.

T.A.C.T. offers an entirely new perspective in the way we communicate with each other. Our patterns of communication are set up by the time we are three years old, and do not change much after that. We refine our language and learn more as we go along, but what we learn in many cases is methods of communication which bring about the opposite result to the one we want.

In our strife torn world, divorce, workers versus management, juvenile delinquency, increasing crimes of violence, all point to a drastic lack of loving communication. Society does not offer classes in the art, it is not taught in schools, and parents cannot pass on what they do not know.

Respect, acceptance and communication are the foundations of a loving relationship. Kinesiology is a method of communication. Kinesiology is a way to share loving communication with others.

How to get more information.

Since the first printing of this book in 1995, nearly twenty-five years of exponential growth in technology have flown by. The truths in this book concerning kinesiology have not changed, and are still of great value to those who make use of them.

However over that time, a vast amount of careful research into more applications of Advanced Kinesiology by top Chiropractic doctors has led to the discovery of a large number of powerful new techniques.

The Academy of Systematic Kinesiology has incorporated many of these very useful, effective and powerful methods into their Foundation Courses and the Practitioner training programmes.

Please go to the T.A.S.K. website:

www.kinesiology.co.uk

The Academy of Systematic Kinesiology

The Academy trains both lay people and health professionals how to use pure authentic 'Systematic Kinesiology' which is a unique and effective holistic approach to enhance health and well-being in everyday life.

Leading the way since 1985, the Academy has highly skilled experts who teach high-calibre Foundation and Advanced Kinesiology courses.

A progressive introduction to Kinesiology, suitable for beginners and also for practitioners who wish to integrate it with other therapies, The Foundation Course may be taken either as 6 weekends or 2 Wednesdays a month over a six-month period.

There are two Practitioner Courses comprising 10 modules, available either at weekends or weekdays over an eight-month period. On graduation you will qualify as a registered 'Systematic Kinesiologist'.

Please view the T.A.S.K. website:
www.kinesiology.co.uk